Have a Jolly Birthday Emma!
8 yrs young today!
Lots of Love from Granny
and Grandad.
xx♡xx

nickelodeon

JoJo Siwa™

Annual 2018

JoJo Siwa: Annual
A CENTUM BOOK 978-1-912396-03-0
Published in Great Britain by Centum Books Ltd
This edition published 2017
1 3 5 7 9 10 8 6 4 2

Centum Books Ltd, 20 Devon Square,
Newton Abbot, Devon, TQ12 2HR, UK
books@centumbooksltd.co.uk
CENTUM BOOKS Limited Reg. No. 07641486
A CIP catalogue record for this book is
available from the British Library
Printed in Italy

Centum

Contents

Check out some of the *awesome* things inside this book!

DREAM CRAZY BIG

All About Your Selfie

Write down five unique and awesome things you love about JoJo, then fill in the boxes with five brilliant things that make you unique and totally you!

Five unique things I love about JoJo are:

1.

2.

3.

4.

5.

8

Five unique things about me are:

1.

2.

3.

4.

5.

Stick in a photo of you here:

Draw a bow for JoJo:

9

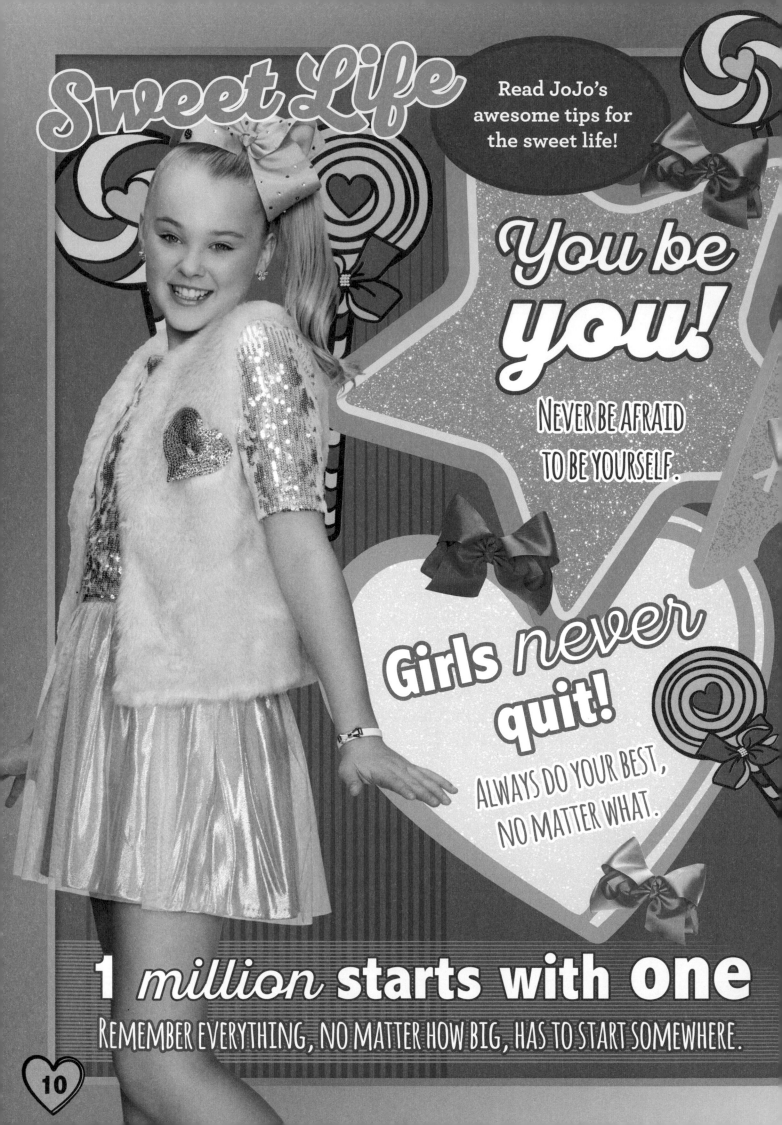

Sweet Life

Read JoJo's awesome tips for the sweet life!

You be you!

NEVER BE AFRAID TO BE YOURSELF.

Girls never quit!

ALWAYS DO YOUR BEST, NO MATTER WHAT.

1 million starts with one

REMEMBER EVERYTHING, NO MATTER HOW BIG, HAS TO START SOMEWHERE.

10

Chill out

It's important to take some quiet time for yourself.

Be beautiful

BEAUTY COMES FROM THE INSIDE, SO SHINE FROM WITHIN.

Besties not Bullies

ALWAYS BE A FRIEND TO PEOPLE AND SHOW THEM KINDNESS.

Be cute and crazy

BE BOTH! BE WHATEVER YOU WANT TO BE.

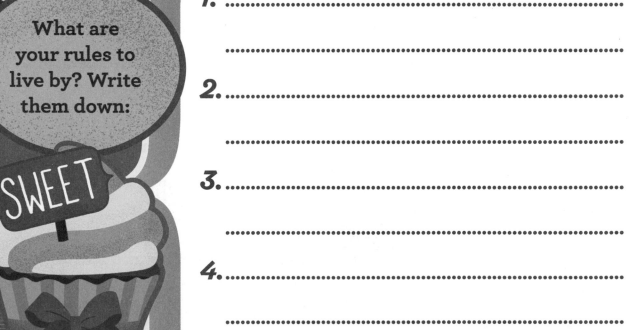

What are your rules to live by? Write them down:

SWEET

1. ....
....
2. ....
....
3. ....
....
4. ....
....
5. ....
....

JoJo's Song Writing Tips

If you were going to write your own song, what would you write about? Use the tips on this page to develop your own lyrics on the opposite page.

First make up the song title.

A song title should:

★ Tell you what the song is about

★ Sound really cool when you say it out loud

★ Express an attitude or emotion

Now, think about an idea or theme.

A good song idea should:

★ Make it clear who is singing

★ Make sure your audience know what you are singing about

★ Make sure everyone knows why exactly you are singing

Music or words?

You might have a tune in your head already and know exactly what the melody will be, or you might just have a beat in mind. If not don't worry, sometimes the lyrics come first and the music comes later.

CUTE & CONFIDENT

12

Your Lyrics

Circle your style of song.

MOOD:
Sad
Happy
Excited
Hopeful
Uplifting

BEAT:
Rock
Hip Hop
Pop
Ballad
Dance

SWEET

Now write your lyrics below:

TITLE:

VERSE 1:

VERSE 2:

CHORUS:

Make a Music Video!

Imagine you're shooting your own music video for the song you wrote on page 13 – develop your video ideas on these pages.

BE YOU

LOCATION:

DID YOU KNOW THAT SEARCHING FOR A LOCATION IS CALLED A LOCATION SCOUT!?

Choose a location from this list or come up with your own.

School ♡
Home ♡
Garden ♡
Park ♡
Beach ♡
Forest ♡
City ♡

Other: ....

....

....

....

....

....

WHO:

Choose who will feature in your video.

Besties ♡
Family ♡
Sports Team ♡
JoJo ♡

Other: ....

....

....

....

....

....

....

DREAM BELIEVE ACHIEVE

JOJO'S VIDEO FOR BOOMERANG WAS FILMED IN A SCHOOL AND KID IN CANDY STORE WAS FILMED IN... YOU GUESSED IT A SWEET SHOP!

DID YOU KNOW that filming a video is only the beginning of the work? Once a video is filmed an editor will take all the clips and put them together to create the final cut.

IMPORTANT JOBS:

Who will fill these important roles on your shoot?

Director (shouts "lights, camera, action!"):

....

Videographer (films with the camera):

....

Sound (keeps the song queued and ready to play):

....

Lighting (makes sure it's not too bright or dark):

....

Choreographer (creates the dance routines):

....

Super Cute

Style and Props

PROPS ARE PERFECT FOR:

★ Super selfies
★ Sleepover fun
★ Making your very own music video!

Now it's time to think about the prop selection and style of your video!

VIDEO PROPS

Did you know that the Production Team will source all the props for video shoots?

It's their job to make videos look extra-special.

HAPPY THOUGHTS

SUPER CUTE

How cool would it be to work on one of JoJo's music videos!?

YOU CAN MAKE YOUR OWN JOJO-INSPIRED PROPS ON PAGE 29 USING THE TEMPLATES ON PAGES 25-28.

Now it's time to pick your props and style your shoot.

First choose your colour palette by circling the colours:

Circle your favourite props below.

Super Cute

DANCE LIKE YOU MEAN IT

CUTE & CONFIDENT

SWEET

SWEET

HAPPY THOUGHTS

SUPER CUTE

DREAM Crazy BIG

Now style your shoot by colouring in the fashion templates.

T-SHIRT

TROUSERS

SKIRT

DRESS

SHOES

17

Storyboard It!

Now work out the scenes in your video — this is called storyboarding. Doodle the action or write notes in each square. What will happen in your video? Tell the story.

DANCE LIKE YOU MEAN IT

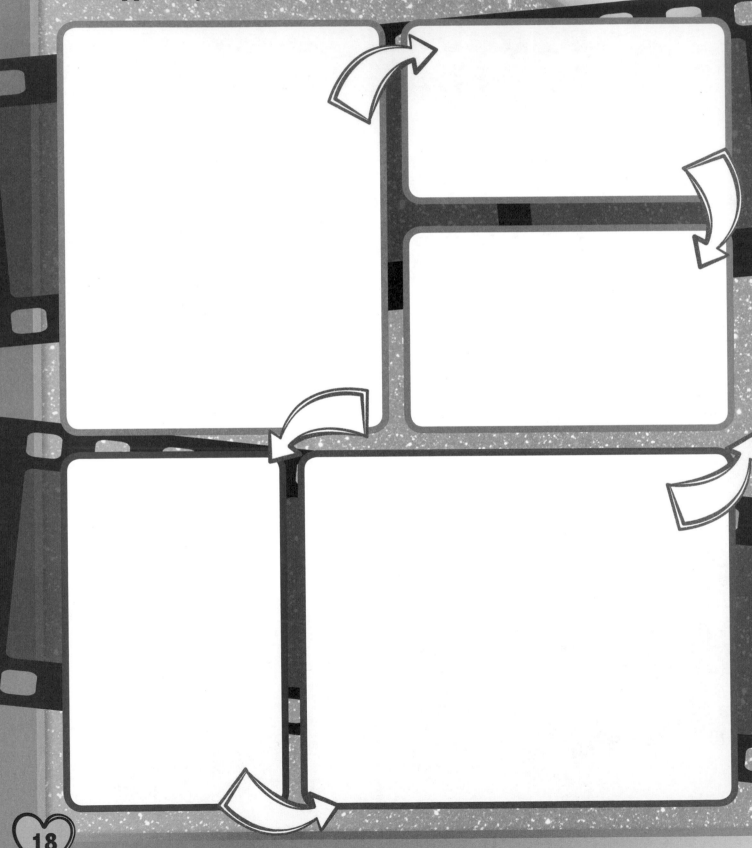

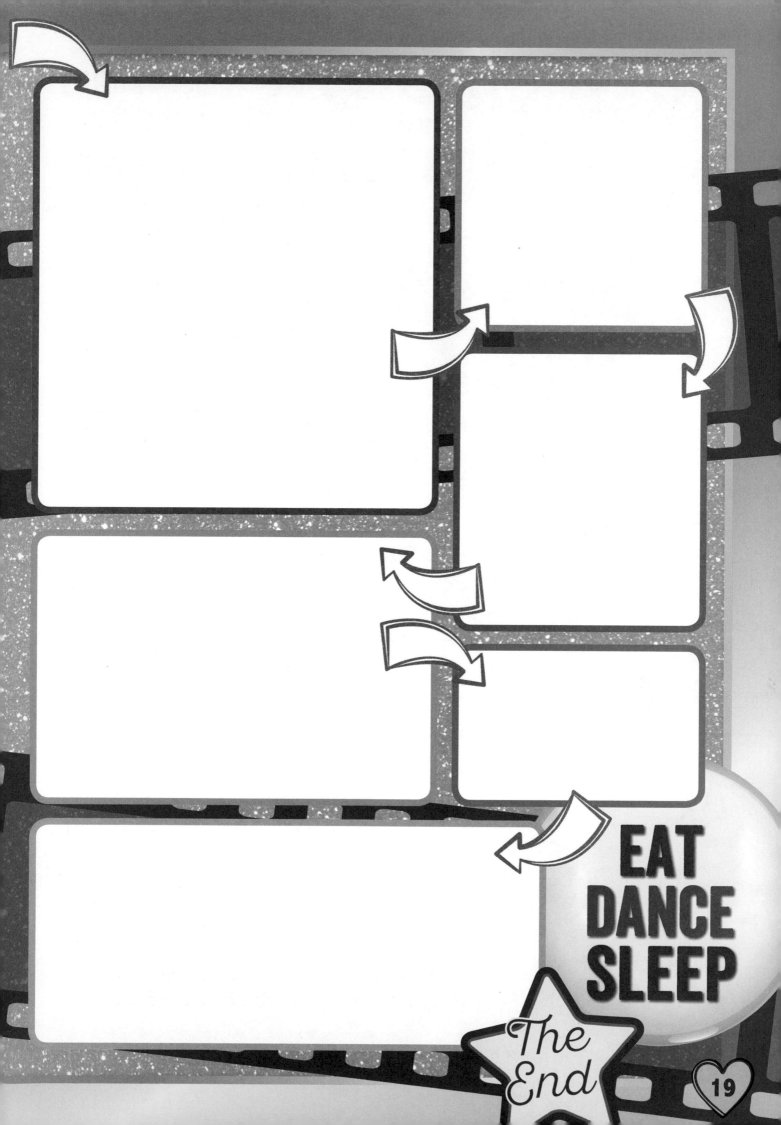

EAT
DANCE
SLEEP

The
End

19

Bow Bracelets

OMG! Bows really are everything. Make these sweet paper bracelets for you and your besties.

THIS IS A PERFECT ACTIVITY FOR A SLEEPOVER!

Always ask a grown-up's permission before using scissors and glue.

YOU WILL NEED:

★ Scissors
★ Glue and tape

STEPS:

Step 1: Remove the page opposite by cutting along the dashed line.

Step 2: Cut out the bracelet strips.

Step 3: Cut out all the bows.

Step 4: Arrange the bows of your choice onto the bracelet of your choice and stick them down using glue.

Tip: Every couple of centimetres will look good!

Step 5: Now strap the bracelet around your wrist and fix in place with a piece of tape.

BOWS ARE MY SUPER POWER

Positivity Poster
Colour in and cut out!
Dream
Believe
ACHIEVE
© Viacom

DANCE LIKE YOU MEAN IT

CUTE & CONFIDENT

HAPPY THOUGHTS

SWEET

SWEET

SUPER CUTE

DREAM *Crazy* BIG

Make Awesome Props!

Follow these instructions to make props that are perfect for selfies, sleepovers or for making your very own music video!

STEP 1
First, remove the prop pages using scissors.

STEP 2
Now stick each page down onto a piece of A4 card using glue.

To ensure the pages dry flat, try lying some books on top.

STEP 3
When dry, take your scissors and cut out each prop.

STEP 4:
Attach a straw to each prop using pieces of tape.

STEP 5:
Now your props are ready, there's only one thing for it,

For some props, you might want to stick the straws on one side, rather than the middle.

POSE UP A STORM!

Picture Perfect

Read these simple rules for taking the best pictures, then experiment taking better shots using your JoJo props.

1. Clean the lens on your phone or camera. Dust and dirt can make your photos misty.

2. Don't take pictures in low light – if you can't see something, then the camera won't either.

3. Avoid bright reflections such as shiny windows, mirrors and plastic surfaces.

4. Keep your subject big and the main focus of your picture. It's sometimes good to focus on one thing for maximum impact.

5. Keep your background free from mess for crisp, clean shots.

6. Use a flash, only if necessary – natural-light is way more pleasing to the eye.

7. Frame your shot. Think of your screen as a cross-section of lines to help you get everything centred. Something like this:

8. Use a backdrop when shooting objects or poses to make things really stand out.

Stick in a picture that you are very proud of showing you using your props!

Positive Words

JoJo's positive attitude is infectious. Can you work out what the uplifting words are below by unscrambling the letters?

BEE LIVE

FENCED COIN

AM RED

NUF

LEG GIG

GUH

AGE MINI

KEOJ

HUG LA

KATL

See answers on page 69.

32

Flag
Colouring

Fold

Fold

Fold

Colour in these flags, then
cut them out and attach them
to straws or craft sticks, or turn
them into bunting. They make awesome
decorations for your bedroom or study!

Happy Thoughts

Doodle the first thing that comes into your head in each shape after reading the prompts below. Don't hesitate; draw whatever you think of first!

Laugh

Dance

Friends

Family

BowBow

Road Trip

Photo Booth

Funny Fill-in

Have some laughs with this funny fill-in challenge. Write down the words in the list below, then fill in the blanks opposite with the words you came up with and reveal a cute and crazy letter!

1. A CITY ....

2. TYPE OF BUILDING ....

3. A PLACE ....

4. AN ANIMAL ....

5. AN ACTIVITY ....

6. TYPE OF FOOD ....

7. AN ITEM TO WEAR ....

8. A PLACE ....

9. AN ACTIVITY ....

10. A FAMOUS PERSON ....

....

36

JOJO WOULD **100%** LOVE IT!

From My **Heart** To **Yours**

HELLO FROM SUNNY

(1) ....!

I'VE RECENTLY ARRIVED AT MY (2) ....

TODAY WE WENT TO THE (3) .... AND I SAW

LOTS OF (4) .... TOMORROW I AM GOING

TO (5) .... AND WE WILL EAT LOTS OF

(6) .... I'M SO EXCITED TO GO SHOPPING.

I HOPE TO BUY (7) .... AND CAN'T WAIT TO

WEAR IT TO (8) .... WHERE I WILL BE

(9) .... WITH (10) ....

....

THAT'S ALL FROM ME!

JOJO x

Colour Like Crazy!

Colour in all the sweet treats on these pages and go crazy!

SWEET

Musical Match-up

Look at the big microphone picture below, then search the page opposite to find the one that matches it exactly.

BE YOUR OWN Star

40

a.

b.

c.

d.

e.

f.

g.

h.

i.

j.

k.

l.

See answers on page 69.

Super-Fan Crossword

Complete this JoJo super-fan crossword. How much do you know about JoJo?

DOWN

1. Which state in the USA is JoJo from?
2. What is JoJo short for?
4. What's the name of her dog?
9. At what age did JoJo dance her first solo?
5. What does JoJo always wear in her hair?
6. What was the name of JoJo's hit single?
7. What's the name of her YouTube channel?
8. What does JoJo call her fans?

ACROSS

3. Which type of dance does JoJo dislike?

SUPER CUTE

Bow Hunt

JoJo can't find the bow she wants to wear. Follow the instructions and find it.

Start your quest in square A10.

MOVE:

1. **3 squares East**
2. **5 squares North**
3. **2 squares West**
4. **3 squares North**
5. **7 squares East**
6. **4 squares South**

Answer:

....

N W E S

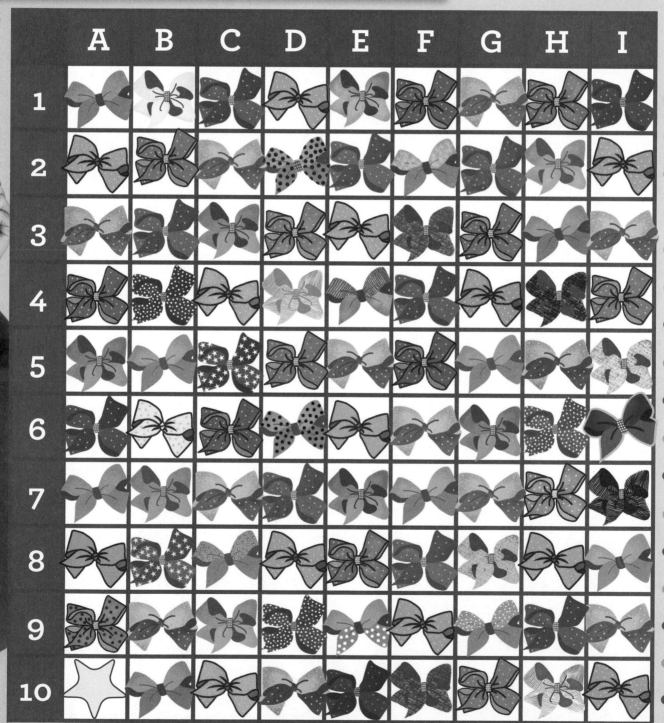

See answers on page 69.

a.

b.

c.

d.

e.

f.

g.

h.

i.

j.

See answers on page 69.

TIP: THERE ARE MORE SHADOWS THAN THERE ARE POSES!

45

Dream Journal

Ever wondered what your dreams might mean? Keep this book by your bedside with a pen and write down any dreams you remember until all the boxes are filled.

DREAM 1

DREAM 2

DREAM 3

DREAM 4

DREAM 5

DREAM 6

DREAM 7

DREAM 8

DREAM 9

DREAM 10

DREAM 11

DREAM 12

FIND OUT WHAT YOUR DREAMS MIGHT MEAN ON THE NEXT PAGE!

What do your dreams mean?

FALLING DREAMS
If you dream you are falling, from the sky, down a hole or off a cliff, it can mean you feel out of control. Try to work out what area of your life you need to take control of, and what you can do about it, and these dreams will stop.

What do you dream about most? (tick one)

- SCHOOL
- CELEBS
- FRIENDS
- GHOSTS
- FILMS
- FAMILY

FLYING DREAMS
If you dream you are flying it means you feel confident and secure about your life and in control. If you dream you are flying too high it can mean you are concerned how your success might change your life.

NO CLOTHES!
Ever dream you've forgotten to put your clothes on? It usually means you're feeling a bit worried about something. It can also mean you are trying to hide your true self.

DREAM Crazy BIG

JoJo dreamt of becoming a star when she was just a little girl and worked hard to turn her dream into reality. Use the space below to write about your dreams for the future.

My Dream:

JOB

....
....

HOLIDAY

....
....

OUTFIT

....
....

DAY

....
....

MEAL

....
....

Dance Dictionary

Have you heard some dance terms and wondered what they mean? Then read JoJo's dance dictionary!

ARM STYLING
Positioning and movement of the arms, matching the character and style of the dance.

BACKFLIP
A dancer flips over backwards. Usually this is followed by a frontflip.

BALLET
Classical theatrical dancing based on the danse d'école, the rules and vocabulary that were created around 1700 in France.

BALLROOM DANCES
Social dances usually performed by couples, including the foxtrot, waltz, tango, rumba, swing, mambo, samba and cha-cha.

BARRE
The wooden bar that runs around the wall of the ballet studio at waist height, which the dancer holds onto during the first part of class.

BREAKING
Dancing with floor movements, such as spins, freezes and poses.

CHOREOGRAPHY
A series of steps, patterns and movements that make up a dance or a dance routine.

HEADSPIN
In a headstand position, the dancer spins by pushing with the hands.

LINE
The length and stretch of the body from head to toe.

MODERN DANCE
A form of dance that expresses complex emotions and ideas.

PIROUETTE
A complete turn of the body on one leg in ballet. The other leg is placed with the foot pointing up to the ankle or knee of the supporting leg.

POINT
A position in ballet on the tip of the toes.

POSITIONS
In ballet, there are basic positions for the feet and arms from which all steps begin and end.

EAT DANCE SLEEP

Dance Routine

Design your own JoJo-inspired dance routine in the boxes below. Remember you need to have a big finish!

STEP 1		STEP 2		STEP 3		STEP 4	
STEP 5		STEP 6		STEP 7		STEP 8	
STEP 9		STEP 10		STEP 11		STEP 12	
STEP 13		STEP 14		STEP 15		STEP 16	
STEP 17		STEP 18		STEP 19		STEP 20	

Musical Notes

Count the musical notes below. How many of each kind are there?

See answers on page 69.

53

What's Your Dance Style?

What type of dance best matches your personality? Find out by answering the questions below, then turn the page to reveal the answers.

ASK YOUR BESTIE TO DO THE QUIZ AND SEE HOW YOU COMPARE!

1. How would you describe your style?

a) Cool and comfy.

b) The latest trends.

c) Something that sparkles.

d) Floral and floaty.

2. Select your favourite colour from the options below.

a) Blue is best!

b) Team green!

c) Gold or silver!

d) Definitely pink!

3. What do you do after school?

a) Grab some snacks.

b) Hang out with friends.

c) Watch YouTube.

d) Clubs or homework.

4. What's important to you in a song?

a) The drums, you can't have a song without a beat.

b) For me, it's all about the lyrics.

c) It's 100% about the routine.

d) How a song makes you feel is SO important.

5. What's the best thing about dancing?

a) The music!

b) Practising new moves and nailing it.

c) My family seeing me perform.

d) I love rehearsing until everything is perfect.

6. Which of these could you never live without?

a) My headphones.

b) My dance crew.

c) My dance gear.

d) My dance teacher.

Number of:	As	Bs	Cs	Ds
Me	♥	♥	♥	♥
Bestie	♥	♥	♥	♥

55

Quiz Answers

Now find out what type of dancer you are!

Mostly As

You're a break-dancer! Even though you might be relaxed when it comes to practice, you're fun, sporty, and effortlessly cool.

Mostly Bs

You're a hip hop dancer! You're popular, fashionable and confident, so get ready to pop and lock!

Mostly Cs

You're a tap dancer! You're fun to be around and a great person. Your friends trust you 100%.

Mostly Ds

You're a ballerina! You're graceful and a great friend! You love working hard – so ballet is perfect for you!

Dance Wordsearch

Find these dance-related words in the grid below!
Can you find them all?

BALLET
BREAKDANCE
CONTEMPORARY
COUNTRY
FLAMENCO
FOLK
FOXTROT
HIP HOP

JAZZ
JIVE
LATIN
MODERN
QUICKSTEP
TAP
WALTZ

A	S	V	K	Y	Q	U	I	C	K	S	T	E	P	O
B	M	L	U	W	C	N	R	E	H	E	X	F	Z	K
R	O	F	A	X	T	P	O	T	L	W	B	J	C	U
F	D	L	Q	C	T	I	H	L	J	L	R	E	O	T
H	R	A	D	J	X	E	A	M	H	N	E	K	U	L
V	A	M	S	G	W	B	E	P	I	Y	A	Q	N	I
T	I	E	M	T	D	C	O	C	P	G	K	U	T	K
J	T	N	A	V	F	Y	I	S	H	X	D	Z	R	H
L	U	C	O	N	T	E	M	P	O	R	A	R	Y	D
A	Q	O	F	P	A	R	W	C	P	K	N	D	I	P
T	N	R	A	T	P	B	F	A	Z	K	C	U	K	J
I	J	G	N	P	W	C	F	V	L	K	E	G	R	I
N	Q	A	M	O	D	E	R	N	X	T	F	S	T	V
X	S	C	Z	Y	W	M	I	S	D	U	Z	J	T	E
I	H	W	P	Z	L	J	F	O	X	T	R	O	T	Z

See answers on page 69.

Find BowBow

JoJo has been away on tour and now it's time to race home to BowBow! She can't wait for a snuggle. Find the way through the maze so they can be reunited.

START

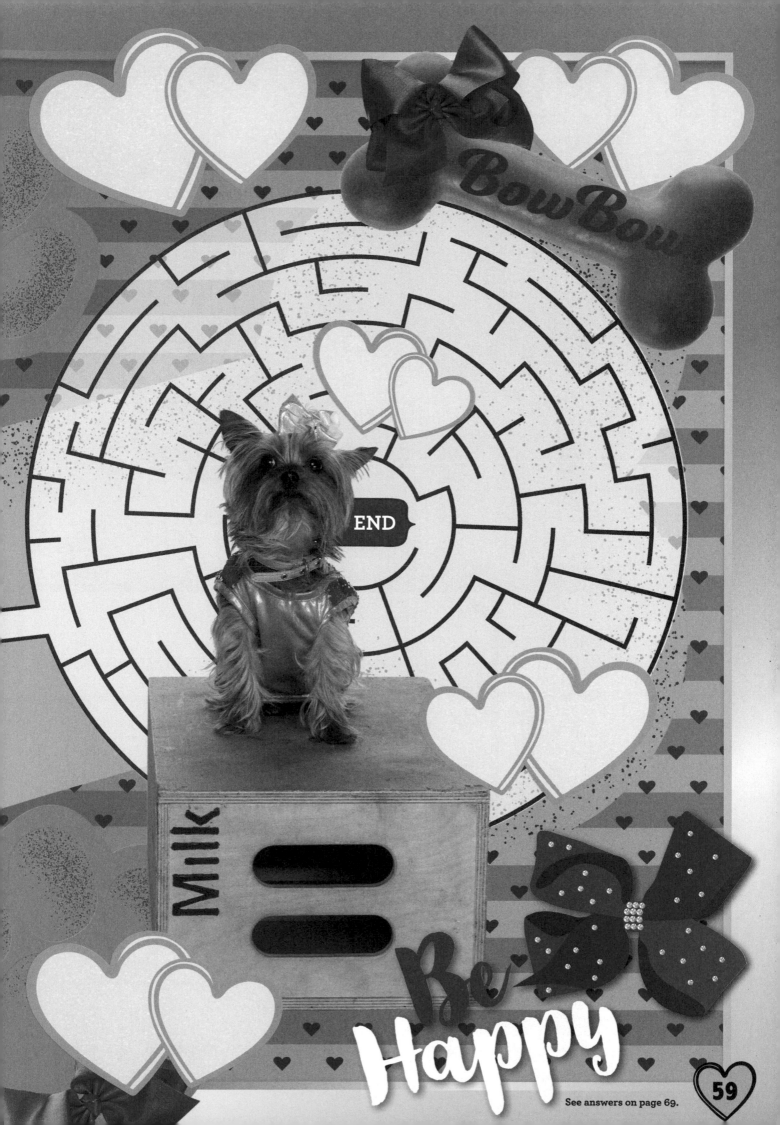

END

BowBow

Milk

Be Happy

See answers on page 69.

Lyric Doodles

Play this doodle game with a friend. Take it in turns to think of a song lyric, then draw it in three doodles. *Have fun guessing the lyrics!*

Do you know any of JoJo's song lyrics?

1

2

3

Guess the lyrics here:

....

....

Now, reveal the lyrics here:

....

....

1

2

3

Guess the lyrics here:

. . . .

. . . .

Now, reveal the lyrics here:

. . . .

. . . .

1

2

3

Guess the lyrics here:

. . . .

. . . .

Now, reveal the lyrics here:

. . . .

. . . .

Cute Patchwork

BowBow should totally make the grid!

Doodle cute things into each square of this grid to create a cute patchwork masterpiece.

My Happy Playlist

JoJo knows that music is an awesome way to get you feeling great. It can literally lift your mood. What songs would you make your happy play list?

A SONG THAT MAKES YOU SMILE:

....

....

A SONG THAT MAKES YOU WANT TO DANCE:

....

....

A SONG THAT REMINDS YOU OF A SUPER-HAPPY TIME:

....

....

A SONG THAT YOU LOVE TO SING:

....

....

A SONG THAT YOU AND YOUR BEST FRIEND BOTH LOVE:

....

....

Doodles

Draw the first thing that comes into your head when you read these hashtags.

#Fun

#JoJoSiwa

#Love

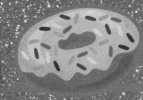
#Summer

#Peachouthaterz

64

#Friends

DREAM
Crazy
BIG

#Happy

HAPPY
THOUGHTS

#Beautiful

65

Chill Out!

Colour in each of these hearts in colours that really chill you out.

Add PATTERNS TOO!

CHILL TIME = ONESIE TIME!

Positivity Cards

Don't you just love JoJo's positive vibes and attitude? If you or a friend aren't feeling 100%, then cut out these positivity cards and read or share one together when you're feeling down.

Be Your Own Star

Feeling Stressed? Dance it OUT

Don't Forget to DREAM CRAZY BIG

STARS ALWAYS SHINE

You're CUTE & CONFIDENT

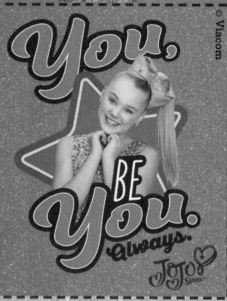

You, BE You. always.

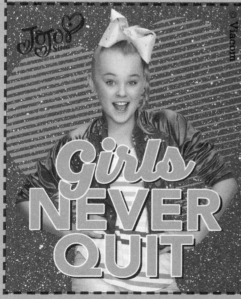

Girls NEVER QUIT

1 Million STARTS WITH ONE

ALWAYS BE YOUR SELFIE

© Viacom

Positivity Cards

Remember if you're feeling down, it's always helpful to tell someone, whether it's a friend, parent or even a teacher. A problem shared is a problem halved. It's good to talk!

Don't Stop Dreaming

TAKE SOME TIME FOR YOU

Dream Together, Friends Forever

You are EVERYTHING!

You're CUTE & Crazy

ALWAYS THERE FOR YOU

Never GIVE UP!

100% LOVE YOURSELF

Today is Your day

© Viacom

Answers

Page 32: Positive Words

BEE LIVE > BELIEVE
FENCED COIN > CONFIDENCE
AM RED > DREAM
NUF > FUN
LEG GIG > GIGGLE
GUH > HUG
AGE MINI > IMAGINE
KEOJ > JOKE
HUG LA > LAUGH
KATL > TALK

Pages 40 and 41: Musical Match-up

The matching picture is F

Page 42: Super-Fan Crossword

Page 43: Bow Hunt

The answer is square I6

Pages 44 and 45:

Dance, Dance, Dance!

1. a;   2. h;   3. j;   4. i;   5. e;   6. c

Page 53: Musical Notes

8   4   4   6   5   2   6

4   5   3   5   5

Page 57: Dance Wordsearch

A	S	V	K	Y	Q	U	I	C	K	S	T	E	P	O
B	M	L	U	W	C	N	R	E	H	E	X	F	Z	K
R	O	F	A	X	T	P	O	T	L	W	B	J	C	U
F	D	L	Q	C	T	I	H	L	J	L	R	E	O	T
H	R	A	D	J	X	E	A	M	H	N	E	K	U	L
V	A	M	S	G	W	B	E	P	I	Y	A	Q	N	I
T	I	E	M	T	D	C	O	C	P	G	K	U	T	K
J	T	N	A	V	F	Y	I	S	H	X	D	Z	R	H
L	U	C	O	N	T	E	M	P	O	R	A	R	Y	D
A	Q	O	F	P	A	R	W	C	P	K	N	D	I	P
T	N	R	A	T	P	B	F	A	Z	K	C	U	K	J
I	J	G	N	P	W	C	F	V	L	K	E	G	R	I
N	Q	A	M	O	D	E	R	N	X	T	F	S	T	V
X	S	C	Z	Y	W	M	I	S	D	U	Z	J	T	E
I	H	W	P	Z	L	J	F	O	X	T	R	O	T	Z

Pages 58 and 59: Find BowBow